INTRODUCTORY COLLEGE MATHEMATICS

Geometric Measures

ROBERT D. HACKWORTH, Ed.D.

Department of Mathematics
St. Petersburg Junior College at Clearwater
Clearwater, Florida

and

JOSEPH HOWLAND, M.A.T.

Department of Mathematics
St. Petersburg Junior College at Clearwater
Clearwater, Florida

S AUNDERS **M** ODULAR
ERIES IN ATHEMATICS

W. B. Saunders Company: West Washington Square
                          Philadelphia, PA 19105

                          12 Dyott Street
                          London, WC1A 1DB

                          833 Oxford Street
                          Toronto, Ontario M8Z 5T9, Canada

INTRODUCTORY COLLEGE MATHEMATICS   ISBN 0-7216-4420-1
Geometric Measures

Last digit is the print number: 9 8 7 6 5 4 3 2 1

PREFACE

Geometric Measures

This book is one of the sixteen content modules in the Saunders Series in Modular Mathematics. The modules can be divided into three levels, the first of which requires only a working knowledge of arithmetic. The second level needs some elementary skills of algebra and the third level, knowledge comparable to the first two levels. *Geometric Measures* is in level 2. The groupings according to difficulty are shown below.

Level 1	Level 2	Level 3
Tables and Graphs	*Numeration*	*Real Number System*
Consumer Mathematics	*Metric Measure*	*History of Real Numbers*
Algebra 1	*Probability*	*Indirect Measurement*
Sets and Logic	*Statistics*	*Algebra 2*
Geometry	*Geometric Measures*	*Computers*
		Linear Programming

The modules have been class tested in a variety of situations: large and small discussion groups, lecture classes, and in individualized study programs. The emphasis of all modules is upon ideas and concepts.

Geometric Measures emphasizes skills in the measurement and computation of lengths, areas, and volume. The module is appropriate for education and liberal arts students. It is also well suited for math-science and technical students. In any case, *Geometric Measures* is appropriate for the freshman or sophomore student.

The module begins by discussing units of measure and the inexactness of every measure. Then *Geometric Measure* develops the concept of maximum and minimum error of measurement. After discussing the concept of perimeter paths and the principle of conservation, the module proceeds to the topics of perimeter, area, and volume of geometric figures.

In preparing each module, we have been greatly aided by the valuable suggestions of the following excellent reviewers: William Andrews, Triton College, Ken Goldstein, Miami-Dade Community College, Don Hostetler, Mesa Community College, Karl Klee, Queensboro Community College, Pamela Matthews, Chabot College, Robert Nowlan, Southern Connecticut State College, Ken Seydel, Skyline College, Ara Sullenberger, Tarrant County Junior College, and Ruth Wing, Palm Beach Junior College. We thank them, and the staff at W. B. Saunders Company for their support.

Robert D. Hackworth
Joseph W. Howland

NOTE TO THE STUDENT

OBJECTIVES:

Upon completing this unit the reader is expected to be able to demonstrate the following skills and concepts:

1. an understanding of the approximation involved in every geometric measurement

2. an understanding of the effects of approximate measures on computations of perimeters, areas, and volumes.

3. an ability to find perimeters of polygons and circles

4. an ability to find areas of polygons and circles

5. an ability to find volumes of rectangular solids and cylinders.

Three types of problem sets, with answers, are included in this module. Progress Tests appear at the end of each section. These Progress Tests are always short with three to six problems. The questions asked in Progress Tests always come directly from the material of the section immediately preceding the test.

Exercise Sets appear less frequently in the module. More problems appear in an Exercise Set than in a Progress Test. These problems arise from all sections of the module preceding the Exercise Set. Section I problems in each Exercise Set were chosen to match the objectives of the module. Section II problems of each Exercise Set are challenge problems.

A Self-Test is found at the end of the module. The Self-Test contains problems representative of the entire module.

In learning the material, the student is encouraged to try each problem set as it is encountered, check all answers, and re-study those sections where difficulties are discovered. This procedure is guaranteed to be both efficient and effective.

CONTENTS

Linear Measures...1

Maximum Error of Measurement....................5

Principle of Conservation.......................7

Perimeters.....................................11

Quadrilaterals.................................14

Perimeter Errors Caused by Computations with Measurements...17

The Circle.....................................21

Area Measures..................................28

Other Units for Measuring Areas................32

Errors in Area Computations....................36

Area Formulas..................................38

Areas of Other Polygons and Circles............42

Volume Measures................................48

Rectangular Solids, Cubes, and Cylinders.......51

Module Self-Test...............................56

Progress Test Answers..........................58

Exercise Set Answers...........................60

Module Self-Test Answers.......................63

Review Exercise Sets...........................64

Review Exercise Set Answers....................69

GEOMETRIC MEASURES

LINEAR MEASURES

The most common and simplest type of geometric measure is called
a linear measure. Direct linear measurements are often made
with devices such as rulers, tape measures, and meter sticks.
Each of the line segments shown in Figure 1 could be measured by
a ruler or meter stick.

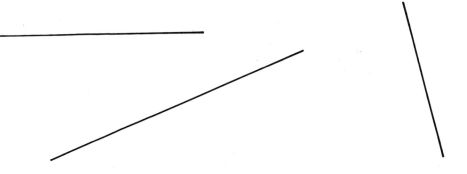

Figure 1

Each of the preceding figures is a straight line segment, but
linear measures are not limited by the "straightness" of the
geometric figures. The length of each of the lines in Figure 2
can also be described by a linear measure.

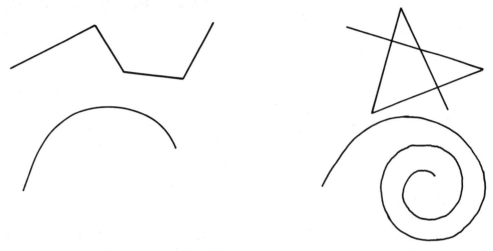

Figure 2

Measuring the "paths" or "curves" of Figure 2 may pose difficulties for those who believe linear measurements must be applied
only to straight lines, but the concept of linear measures is
more concerned with length than it is with a consistency of
direction.

The central idea of linear measure is length or distance. It is
best learned by actually measuring the lengths of some line segments. Below is a line segment with a ruler shown directly be-
neath it.

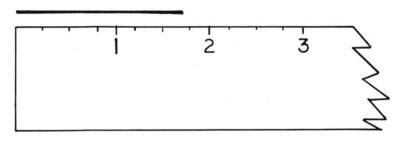

Figure 3

Figure 3 shows a ruler with its 1 and 2 inch marks clearly
labeled. There are, however, other marks on the ruler in addi-
tion to the inch marks. These other marks on the ruler are very
important because they, not the inch marks, indicate the unit of
measurement for this particular ruler. To determine the unit of

measure, count the number of equal spaces between the 1-inch and 2-inch marks. Since there are four spaces the unit of measure is $\frac{1}{4}$ inches or quarter/inches. The line segment of Figure 3 ends nearest to the third mark between 1-inch and 2-inch. The line segment's "correct" measurement in Figure 3 is $1\frac{3}{4}$ inches.

In Figure 4 is a line segment with the same length as that in Figure 3. This time the ruler is marked differently. That is, the ruler has a different unit of measure.

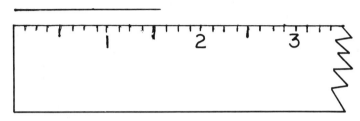

Figure 4

What is the unit of measure for the ruler in Figure 4? What is the correct measurement for the line segment in Figure 4? The correct answer for the first question is $\frac{1}{8}$ inch because there are eight spaces between the 1-inch and 2-inch marks. The "correct" measurement is $1\frac{5}{8}$ inches because the nearest (closest) mark to the end of the line segment is the fifth mark between the 1-inch and 2-inch labels.

The reader may be puzzled by the fact that the line segment of Figure 3 was "correctly" measured as $1\frac{3}{4}$ inches, but the same segment measured in Figure 4 had a "correct" measurement of $1\frac{5}{8}$ inches. This discrepancy illustrates a fact about measurements that is rarely understood. The "correctness" of a linear measure is relative to the use of a common unit of measure. Two measures of the same length using the same unit of measure should be equal, but two measures of the same length using two different units of measure will be different. Unequal measures for the same length?? That is true. All measurements are approximations, their accuracy determined by their units of measure. Therefore, measurements using different units of measure will provide different, unequal, approximations.

The measurement of a line segment with a ruler marked in half-inches may be $7\frac{1}{2}$ inches, but that is an approximation. The same line segment, if measured with a ruler marked off in tenths of an inch, may be 7.4 inches long. Both measurements may be correct with respect to the rulers used. Both measures are approximations because the accuracy is limited by the sizes of the units of measure.

In Figure 5 is shown a portion of a meter stick and a ruler using $\frac{1}{16}$ inch as its unit of measure. Use the ruler and try to find the exact measure of 6 centimeters.

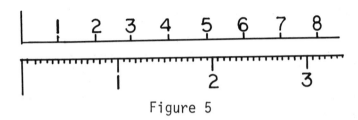

Figure 5

$2\frac{5}{16}$ or $2\frac{6}{16}$ inches are answers that might be read from Figure 5 for a length of 6 centimeters. These answers are approximations. By conversion tables, correct 4 decimal places, for changing centimeters to inches, 6 centimeters is approximately 2.3622 inches. The reader using the ruler of Figure 5 will arrive at an approximation for 6 cm that is both different from 2.3622 inches and less accurate.

To sum up, or review, the measuring concepts previously discussed, the learner should now know: (1) all measurements are approximations, (2) the degree of accuracy of a measurement is dependent upon the size of the unit of measure.

Exact numbers are never the result of measurements. Counting objects is a method of generating exact answers, but measures are always approximations.

___

Progress Test 1

1.   The number 100 is an approximation for which of the following:
     a.   There are 100 members in the United States Senate.
     b.   The boys raced 100 yards.

True or false?

2.   Two people using differently marked rulers may correctly measure the same line segment and arrive at different answers.

3. Two people using the same ruler may correctly measure the same line segment and arrive at different answers.

4. There is an error involved in every measurement.

MAXIMUM ERROR OF MEASUREMENT

The next measuring concept to be presented is the maximum error in a measurement. Using a ruler marked off in $\frac{1}{8}$ inch units, the ruler measures to the nearest $\frac{1}{8}$ inch. Using a ruler marked off in units of one centimeter, the ruler measures to the nearest one centimeter. In both cases, as well as all measuring situations, the measurement will be an approximation. However, the maximum degree of error in the measurement can always be established from the unit of measurement. Since measurements are made to the nearest unit, the maximum error in a correctly made measurement is plus or minus one-half the unit of measure. For example, when using $\frac{1}{2}$ inch as a unit, the maximum error is $\frac{1}{2} \cdot \frac{1}{2}$ or $\frac{1}{4}$ inch. The segments in Figure 6 should all be correctly labeled 2 inches long, even though the longest may actually be $2\frac{1}{4}$ inches long and the shortest $1\frac{3}{4}$ inches long, the three segments in Figure 6 are all 2 inches long using the ruler shown. Notice that the segments can vary as much as $\frac{1}{4}$ inch on either side of the 2-inch mark and still be called 2 inches long.

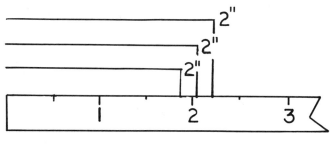

Figure 6

When $\frac{1}{2}$ inch is the unit the segments will not be correctly labeled 2 inches long if they vary more than $\frac{1}{2}$ of $\frac{1}{2}$ or $\frac{1}{4}$ inch from the 2 inch mark.

Using $\frac{1}{8}$ inch as the unit of measure, the maximum error in a measurement is one-half of $\frac{1}{8}$ inch ($\frac{1}{2} \cdot \frac{1}{8}$) or $\frac{1}{16}$ inch. Using one centimeter as the unit of measure, the maximum error in a measurement is one-half of one centimeter ($\frac{1}{2} \cdot \frac{1}{1}$) or $\frac{1}{2}$ cm (5 mm).

The maximum error in a measurement, sometimes called the degree of tolerance, is extremely important to any act of measurement. An amateur gardener planning to plant a row of corn may be willing to accept a measuring error of five feet in establishing the length of his row. With 5 feet as the maximum error of measurement, the gardener could use 10 feet as his unit of measure. One-half of 10 feet ($\frac{1}{2}$ x 10) is 5 feet, the maximum error.

Another way of viewing the problem is that two times 5 feet, the acceptable error, is 10 feet, the unit of measure.

In general, the maximum error of measurement is used to determine the unit of measure. A cabinet maker who can tolerate a maximum error of $\frac{1}{16}$ inch can use $\frac{1}{8}$ inch (2 x $\frac{1}{16}$) as his unit of measure. A machinist who desires a maximum error of 0.0005 inch may use 0.001 inch (2 x 0.0005) as his unit of measure.

In measurements, the numbers $\frac{3}{4}$ inches, $\frac{6}{8}$ inches, and $\frac{12}{16}$ inches have three different meanings. Despite the fact that $\frac{3}{4} = \frac{6}{8} = \frac{12}{16}$, the measurements $\frac{3}{4}$ inch and $\frac{6}{8}$ inch are different because the measurement $\frac{3}{4}$ inch indicates $\frac{1}{4}$ inch as the unit of measure, and the measurement $\frac{6}{8}$ inch indicates $\frac{1}{8}$ inch as the unit of measure.The measurement $\frac{12}{16}$ inch indicates $\frac{1}{16}$ inch as the unit of measure. The measurement $\frac{3}{4}$ inch has $\frac{1}{8}$ inch as the maximum error. $\frac{6}{8}$ inch has $\frac{1}{16}$ inch as the maximum error. $\frac{12}{16}$ inch has $\frac{1}{32}$ inch as the maximum error. $\frac{3}{4}$ inch, $\frac{1}{8}$ inch, and $\frac{12}{16}$ inch are different measurements with different degrees of accuracy.

Unfortunately, many people who communicate linear measurements do not understand and/or practice the ideas discussed here. Consequently, measurements like 200 yards are often mentioned despite the fact that such a measure is very ambiguous with respect to the unit of measured used. 200 yards may mean a unit of 100 yards with an associated maximum error of 50 yards. Then again, it could mean a unit of 10 yards with an associated maximum error of 5 yards. Or again, the 200 yard measurement could have one yard as the unit of measure with an associated maximum error of $\frac{1}{2}$ yard. This ambiguity can be removed from any measure by the by the simple expedient of naming the unit of measure whenever it is not clearly implied by the measurement. If a measurement of 5 feet was acquired with a unit of $\frac{1}{10}$ foot then the accuracy of the measurement could be made clear by the numeral 5.0 feet. If a measurement of 19 feet was acquired with a unit of $\frac{1}{8}$ inch then the accuracy of the measurement could be made clear by the numeral 19 feet, $\frac{0}{8}$ inches.

If a machinist is asked to mill a part with radius 2.0 centimeters, the accuracy of the measure will be to the nearest 0.1 centimeter. If the radius was requested as 2.000 centimeters, the accuracy would be to the nearest 0.001 centimeter. The difference between the accuracy demanded by 2.0 centimeters compared to 2.000 centimeters will be reflected in the machinist's costs.

Progress Test 2

1. If the unit of measure is $\frac{1}{4}$ inch, what is the maximum error of measurement?

2. A carpenter working on a job figured he could allow for a maximum error of measurement of $\frac{1}{2}$ inch. What unit of measure has $\frac{1}{2}$ inch as its maximum error of measurement?

3. Why are $\frac{6}{12}$ inch and $\frac{1}{2}$ inch different measurements?

4. Write the ambiguous measure "30 yards" to show that the unit of measure was one inch.

PRINCIPLE OF CONSERVATION

The last concept of linear measurement to be discussed here is called the Principle of Conservation. The idea behind this concept is that the measure of a linear figure is not altered if it is bent, divided, curved, and/or straightened. For example, an 18.0 inch piece of string may be curled into different curved shapes, wrapped around different shapes, coiled like a spring, or cut into smaller pieces of string, but there still remains 18.0 inches of string.

It is the Principle of Conservation that claims the same linear measurement can be representative of all the shapes shown below in Figure 7.

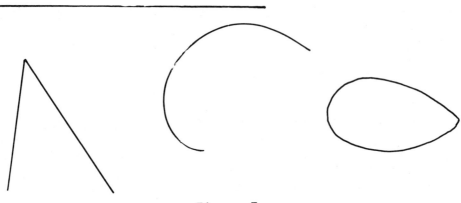

Figure 7

The Principle of Conservation simply states that the linear measure of an inelastic object does not change if the shape of the object is altered.

Progress Test 3

1.   A string is tied into a circle 18 inches around. If the string is cut in one place and stretched out in a line, then how long will it be?

2.   A flat piece of cardboard is 36 centimeters long. If it is folded to form the sides of a square, how far will it be around the outside of the square?

3.   Does the Principle of Conservation apply to a rubber band's length regardless of the shape it forms? Why?

Exercise Set 1

I   1. Determine the unit of measure for each of the following:

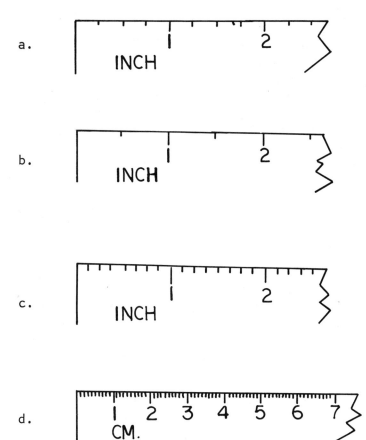

a.

b.

c.

d.

2. Trace the segments below on the edge of a sheet of paper and use the rulers above to measure them.

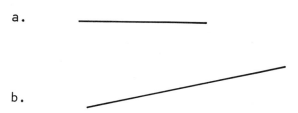

a.

b.

3. Give the maximum error that would exist using the following units of measure:

    a. 1 inch

    b. $\frac{1}{4}$ inch

    c. 1 centimeter

    d. $\frac{1}{32}$ inch

    e. $\frac{1}{8}$ inch

    f. .1 inch

4. For each maximum error given below find the corresponding unit of measure.

    a. $\frac{1}{4}$ inch

    b. .05 inch

    c. $\frac{1}{32}$ inch

    d. $\frac{1}{128}$ inch

    e. $\frac{1}{2}$ meter

    f. .005 centimeter

5. After a pole-vaulter made his vault, the height to the bar was measured with a tape marked off in inches. The height was called 18 feet, 6 inches. Find the lowest and highest the bar could be and still be measured as 18 feet, 6 inches from the ground.

6. The _____ __ _____ states that the length of a piece of string does not change whether the string lies flat on a table or is wound into a ball.

II. Challenge Problems

1. Which of the following are approximations?

    a. John Doe is 5 feet $10\frac{3}{4}$ inches tall.

    b. John Doe scored 100 on a biology test.

    c. John Doe had blood pressure of 140 over 80.

    d. John Doe has 27 classmates in his mathematics course.

2. a. Use Figure 5 to measure the length of 3 centimeters on the ruler.

    b. 3 cm is approximately 1.1813 inches. If 1.1813 inches is not your answer to part a, explain the difference.

3. Which is more accurate, a measurement made in 0.1 inches or a measurement made in 0.1 centimeters? Why?

4. If a ruler is marked in half-inches and a line segment appears to end exactly at the 4 inch mark, how should its measure be written?

5. A munitions factory worker is making parts for bombs. The acceptable margin of error is 0.001 of an inch. What unit of measure should be used to guarantee staying within the margin of error?

PERIMETERS

Sometimes a linearly measured figure is called a path. If a person were to place the point of a pencil on a piece of paper and then move the pencil along the surface of that paper the mark left by the pencil describes the "path" followed by the pencil. Similarly, every linear figure can be thought of as a path.

In Figure 8 six linear paths are shown. Three of the paths are called "perimeter paths" because any point on the path could serve as both the starting <u>and</u> the ending point without tracing any part of the path <u>more</u> than one time.

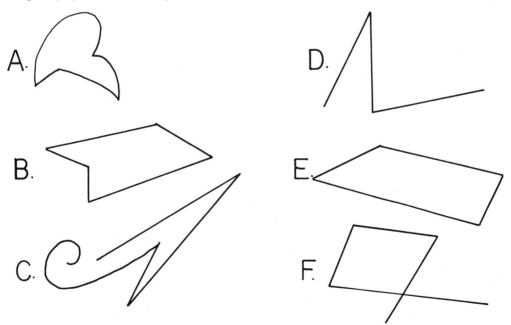

Figure 8

Figures A, B, and E are perimeter paths. Each of them has the properties that (1) Any point on the path can serve as both the starting and ending point of the path, and (2) no point of the path would be traced twice. Figures C, D, and F are not perimeter paths because the figures do not have the required properties.

Whenever a geometric figure is a perimeter path then the linear measure of the path is called its perimeter. In general, this means that the distance around a geometric figure is its perimeter. The figure must have an interior bounded by its path and the length of that path is the perimeter.

Four triangles are shown below in Figure 9.

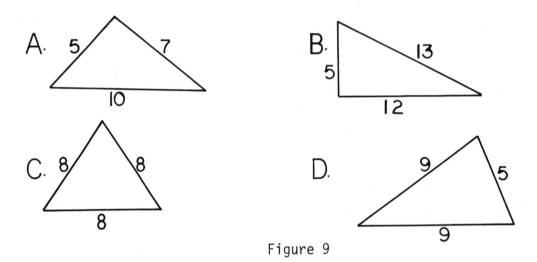

Figure 9

The perimeter of each triangle in Figure 9 is found by adding the lengths of the three sides. This is because of the Principle of Conservation. The perimeter of each triangle is equal to the sum of its three sides.

The perimeter of triangle A is 5 + 7 + 10 or 22. The perimeter of triangle B is 5 + 13 + 12 or 30.

In general the perimeter, P,of a triangle is found by using the formula P = a + b + c where a, b, and c represent the lengths of the three sides.

Two special triangles have somewhat simpler formulas for their perimeters. A triangle which has all of its sides the same length is called an equilateral triangle. Since all three sides of an equilateral triangle are equal, the perimeter formula for such a triangle is often written as P = 3s where s is the length of one of the equal sides. Triangle C in Figure 9 is an equilateral triangle with its perimeter 3 · 8 or 24.

Equilateral triangles are also frequently called equiangular or regular triangles. "Equilateral" is a word describing equal sides. "Equiangular" means equal angles, and "regular" means both equal sides and equal angles. For a triangle, the three terms equilateral, equiangular, and regular describe the same object. This is not the case with four sided figures as will be shown later.

An isosceles triangle is a triangle with at least two equal sides. The perimeter formula for an isosceles triangle is P = 2s + b where s stands for the length of each of the equal sides and b stands for the length of the unequal sides. In Figure 9 triangle D is an isosceles triangle and its perimeter is 2 · 9 + 5 or 23.

Progress Test 4

1.   Which of the following is a perimeter path?

A. 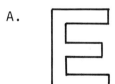   B.

2.   Find the perimeter of each triangle.

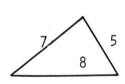   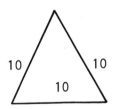

3.   An equilateral triangle is equiangular and _____

QUADRILATERALS

Figure 10 shows five four-sided geometric figures.

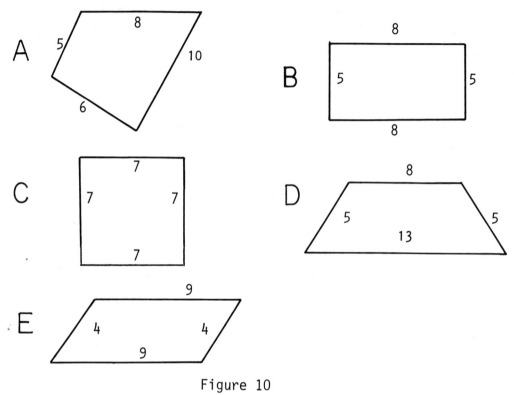

Figure 10

A four-sided geometric figure is called a quadrilateral. In general, the perimeter of a quadrilateral is found by adding the four lengths of the four sides. The general formula for finding the perimeter of a quadrilateral is P = a + b + c + d where a, b, c, and d represent the lengths of the four sides. Using the formula, the perimeter of quadrilateral A in Figure 10 is 5 + 8 + 10 + 6 or 29.

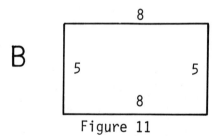

Figure 11

Quadrilateral B in Figure 11 is a rectangle. A rectangle is an equiangular quadrilateral. That is, the four angles of a rectangle are the same size, 90^0. There is an important relationship between the lengths of the opposite sides of every rectangle; the opposite sides are always equal. Consequently, the formula for the perimeter of a rectangle is often written as $P = 2\ell + 2w$ where ℓ stands for the rectangle's length and w for its width. Another formula for the rectangle's perimeter for $P = 2(\ell + w)$. Either formula will give the perimeter for Quadrilateral B. $P = 2 \cdot 8 + 2 \cdot 5$ or $16 + 10$ or 26. $P = 2(8 + 5)$ or $2 \cdot 13$ or 26.

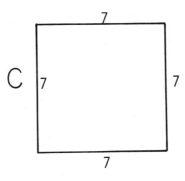

Figure 12

Quadrilateral C in Figure 12 is a square. A square is a regular quadrilateral because it is both equiangular and equilateral. Rectangles are equiangular, but generally not equilateral. It is possible to have a quadrilateral with four equal sides, but without equal angles. For example, a diamond shape is equilateral, but not equiangular. An equilateral four-sided figure that is not equiangular is called a rhombus. Since a square and a rhombus are equilateral the formula for their perimeters is $P = 4s$ where s stands for the length of one of the equal sides. Using the formula $P = 4s$ the perimeter of quadrilateral C in Figure 12 is $4 \cdot 7$ or 28.

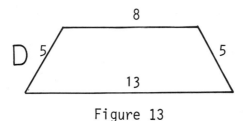

Figure 13

Quadrilateral D in Figure 13 is a trapezoid. A trapezoid is a quadrilateral with one pair of parallel sides. The other pair of sides would not always be equal, but since quadrilateral D does have a pair of equal, opposite sides it is called an isosceles trapezoid. The general formula for the perimeter of

a trapezoid is P = B + b + a + c where B and b stand for the
lengths of the parallel sides and a and c stand for the lengths
of the other two sides. The perimeter of the trapezoid in
Figure 13 is 13 + 8 + 5 + 5 or 31.

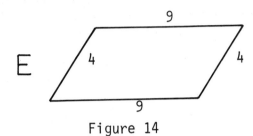

Figure 14

The last quadrilateral to be studied here is shown in Figure 14.
Both pairs of opposite sides for quadrilateral E are parallel.
The quadrilateral is called a parallelogram. One of the important properties of a parallelogram is the fact that the opposite
sides are not only parallel -- they are also equal. Consequently,
if B represents the length of one side of the parallelogram then
B also represents the length of the opposite side. Similarly, if
s represents the length of another side then s also represents
the side opposite it. The perimeter formula P = B + B + s + s
can be simplified.

$$P = B + B + s + s$$

$$P = 2B + 2s$$

$$P = 2(B + s)$$

Either formula, P = 2B + 2s or P = 2(B + s) can be used to find
the perimeter of the parallelogram in Figure 14.

$$P = 2 \cdot 9 + 2 \cdot 4 \qquad\qquad P = 2(9 + 4)$$

$$= 18 + 8 \qquad\qquad\qquad = 2 \cdot 13$$

$$= 26 \qquad\qquad\qquad\qquad = 26$$

Below are listed the perimeter formulas for the triangles and
quadrilaterals discussed in the last two sections.

Triangle	$P = a + b + c$
Isosceles Triangle	$P = 2s + b$
Equilateral Triangle	$P = 3s$
Quadrilateral	$P = a + b + c + d$

Rectangle	$P = 2\ell + 2w$ or $P = 2(\ell + w)$
Square	$P = 4s$
Parallelogram	$P = 2B + 2s$ or $P = 2(B + s)$
Rhombus	$P = 4s$

Progress Test 5

Give the correct name for each quadrilateral and find its parimeter.

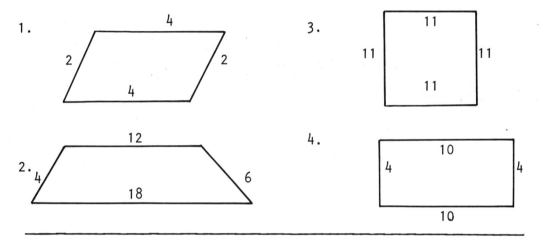

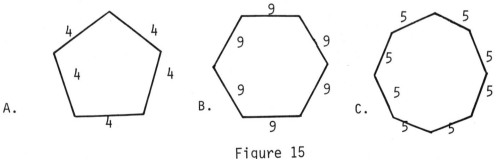

Figure 15

PERIMETER ERRORS CAUSED BY COMPUTATIONS WITH MEASUREMENTS

Below in Figure 15 are shown three more regular polygons.

Polygon A above is a regular pentagon. The word "pentagon" means the polygon has five sides. The word "regular" means that the polygon has equal sides (equilateral) and equal angles

(equiangular). Since the five sides of a regular pentagon are
the same length, the formula for the perimeter of a regular pentagon is P = 5s, where s stands for the length of one of the
equal sides. The perimeter of polygon A is 5 · 4 or 20

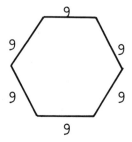

Figure 16

The polygon in Figure 16 is a regular hexagon, a six-sided poly-
gon. The formula for the perimeter of a regular hexagon is
P = 6s, where s stands for the length of one of the equal sides.
The perimeter of the polygon in Figure 16 is 6 · 9 or 54.

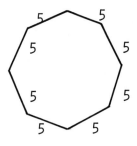

Figure 17

The polygon in Figure 17 is a regular octagon, an eight-sided
polygon. The formula for the perimeter of a regular octagon is
P = 8s, where s stands for the length of one of the equal sides.
The perimeter of the polygon in Figure 17 is 8 · 5 or 40.

Throughout the discussion on perimeters the problems of measurement have been ignored. It is time now to insert a word of caution about using perimeter measures as if they were exact. It
is also time to determine the maximum error involved in computing a polygon's perimeter.

Consider the triangle below in Figure 18.

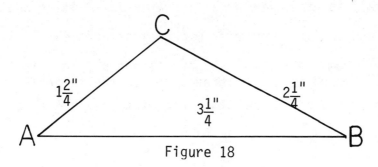

Figure 18

From the measurements indicated on the three sides of △ABC, it can be correctly implied that the unit of measure used was $\frac{1}{4}$ inch. This implication is most clearly shown by side $\overline{AC}$ where the measurement is indicated as $1\frac{2}{4}''$ to purposely make the point that $\frac{1}{4}$ inch is the unit of measure.

Since $\frac{1}{4}$ inch is the unit of measure in Figure 18, the maximum error in measurement is $\frac{1}{8}$ inch ($\frac{1}{2} \cdot \frac{1}{4}$). This means that the actual length of side $\overline{AB}$ is between $3\frac{1}{8}$ inches ($3\frac{1}{4} - \frac{1}{8}$) and $3\frac{3}{8}$ inches ($3\frac{1}{4} + \frac{1}{8}$). Similarly, the actual length of side $\overline{BC}$ is between $2\frac{1}{8}$ inches and $2\frac{3}{8}$ inches. Also, the actual length of side $\overline{AC}$ is between $1\frac{3}{8}$ inches and $1\frac{5}{8}$ inches. These measures and their possible errors are tabulated below.

	Minimum length	Given length	Maximum length
$\overline{AB}$	$3\frac{1}{8}$	$3\frac{1}{4}$	$3\frac{3}{8}$
$\overline{BC}$	$2\frac{1}{8}$	$2\frac{1}{4}$	$2\frac{3}{8}$
$\overline{AC}$	$1\frac{3}{8}$	$1\frac{2}{4}$	$1\frac{5}{8}$
perimeters	$6\frac{5}{8}$	7	$7\frac{3}{8}$

The table shows that it is possible that the perimeter of $\triangle ABC$ is as small as $6\frac{5}{8}$ inches or as large as $7\frac{3}{8}$. Notice that the minimum and maximum perimeter measurements are each $\frac{3}{8}$ inches different from the sum of the given lengths. This is not surprising. Since there are three sides to the triangle and each side had a possible error of $\frac{1}{8}$ inch, the possible error for the perimeter is $\frac{3}{8}$ inch ($3 \times \frac{1}{8}$).

The preceding example is rather extreme because each side of the triangle was separately measured. It is unlikely, though possible, that these three separate measures were all maximum errors on the high or low side. Generally, such separate measures could be expected to have errors that somewhat offset each other but in theory the maximum error for the perimeter of a triangle is three times the maximum error involved in the measure of each separate side.

The theory becomes much more practical in working with regular polygons. This is because the common practice in finding the perimeter of a regular polygon is (1) measure one side, and (2) multiply the measure by the number of sides. For example, consider the square shown below in Figure 19.

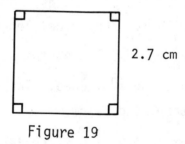

2.7 cm

Figure 19

According to Figure 19, the square has 2.7 cm on one side. Finding the perimeter using the formula P = 4s gives 4 · 2.7 or 10.8 cm. The question now is what is the maximum error in stating the perimeter as 10.8 cm? The answer to that question is determined in two steps'. First, the maximum error in measuring one side must be determined. Since the measurement of 2.7 has .1 as its unit of measurement, the maximum error is $\frac{1}{2}$ · .1 or .05 cm. Second, the maximum error per side is multiplied by the number of sides (4 for a square) to give the maximum error in the perimeter 4 · .05 = .2. .2 cm is the maximum error for the perimeter of the square with one side of measure 2.7 cm.
4(2.7 ± .05) = 10.8 ± .2

In general, the maximum error in computing the perimeter of a polygon is the sum of the maximum errors in measuring the separate sides. With a regular polygon, the maximum error in computing the perimeter is the number of sides times the maximum error in measuring one side.

Progress Test 6

A regular septagon (seven-sided polygon) has one side which is 4.7 meters in length.

  1. Find its perimeter.

  2. Find the maximum error in one side of the septagon's measure.

  3. Find the maximum error in the measure of the septagon's perimeter.

  4. What is the minimum and maximum limits for the true measurement of the septagon's perimeter?

THE CIRCLE

The last plane figure to be presented here is the circle. The length of the boundary line of a circle is not called its perimeter. It is called the circumference, but still means the linear distance of its enclosing line.

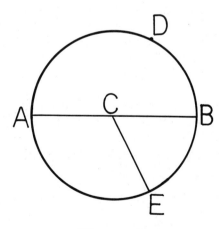

Figure 20

The circumference of the circle in Figure 20 is the distance an object would move if it started at point A and traveled around the circle until it reached point A again.

Point C in Figure 20 represents the center of the circle, which means it is the same distance from every point on the circle. Therefore, the distance from C to A is equal to the distance from C to E or C to B or C to D.

A straight line segment joining the center C to any point on the circle is called a radius. $\overline{CE}$ is a radius, $\overline{CA}$ is a radius. $\overline{CB}$ is a radius, and $\overline{CD}$ is a radius. The plural of radius is radii. Since the center is equidistant from all points on the circle, all radii of a circle are equal.

In Figure 20, the line segment $\overline{AB}$ is called a diameter of the circle. A diameter is a line segment through the center of the circle with endpoints on the circle. Every diameter therefore consists of two radii. Since all radii are equal it can be stated that (1) each diameter is twice the length of a radius, $d = 2r$, and (2) all diameters of a circle are equal.

Returning now to the computation of the circumference (perimeter) of a circle, there is an interesting relationship between the diameter of a circle and its circumference. To understand this relationship, it is necessary to know something about the number called Pi. Pi is an irrational number which means it has a definite position on the number line, but cannot be shown exactly by any mixed number or terminating decimal. Frequently, Pi is approximated by $3\frac{1}{7}$, 3.14 or 3.1416, but these are only approximations because Pi is not exactly equal to any mixed number or terminating decimal.

For over 2000 years man has known that the circumference of a circle, regardless of the circle's size, is equal to Pi times the circle's diameter. This multiplication relationship is shown in the formula $C = \pi d$ where C stands for the circumference, π for Pi, and d for the length of the diameter.

Amother formula for the circumference of a circle is $C = 2\pi r$ where r stands for the radius. The formula $C = 2\pi r$ is obtained from $C = \pi d$ because d is equal to 2r. $C = \pi d$ might be used most easily for finding the circumference of the circle in Figure 21.

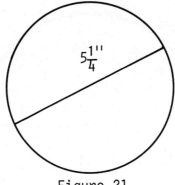

Figure 21

For the circle in Figure 21, the diameter is $5\frac{1}{4}$ inches. Using

the formula C = πd and approximating π by $3\frac{1}{7}$ or 3.14 the compu-

tation of the circumference proceeds as follows:

$$C = 3\frac{1}{7} \cdot 5\frac{1}{4} \qquad\qquad C = 3.14 \cdot 5.25$$

$$= \frac{22}{7} \cdot \frac{21}{4} \qquad\qquad = 16.3850$$

$$= \frac{\overset{11}{\cancel{22}}}{\underset{1}{\cancel{7}}} \cdot \frac{\overset{3}{\cancel{21}}}{\underset{2}{\cancel{4}}} \qquad\qquad = 16.39$$

$$= \frac{33}{2}$$

$$= 16\frac{1}{2}$$

$16\frac{1}{2}$ inches and 16.39 inches are two approximations for the
circumference of the circle in Figure 21.

The maximum error in the circumference answer, $16\frac{1}{2}$ inches, can-

not be exactly stated. This is because the original error in
measuring the diameter, $\frac{1}{2} \cdot \frac{1}{4}$ or $\frac{1}{8}$ inch, has been multiplied by
an approximation for Pi. A satisfactory rule of thumb in this
situation is to multiply the diameter's measuring error by 3,
the closest whole number to Pi. This rule would provide an
approximate error in the circumference of $\frac{3}{8}$ inch. The actual

circumference of the circle probably is between $16\frac{1}{8}$ inches and
$16\frac{7}{8}$ inches.

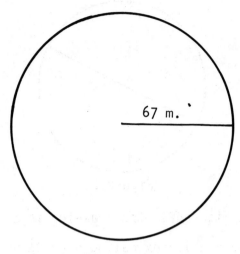

Figure 22

In Figure 22, the radius of the circle is shown to be 67 meters. Using the formula, C = 2πr the circumference may be computed in one of the ways shown below.

Using 3.14 for π	Using 3.1416 for π
C = 2πr	C = 2πr
C = 2 · 3.14 · 67	= 2 · 3.1416 · 67
= 6.28 · 67	= 6.2832 · 67

$$
\begin{array}{r}
6.28 \\
67 \\
\hline
43\ 96 \\
376\ 8 \\
\hline
420.76
\end{array}
\qquad
\begin{array}{r}
6.2832 \\
67 \\
\hline
43\ 9824 \\
376\ 992 \\
\hline
420.9744
\end{array}
$$

Two answers for the circumference are 420.76 meters and 420.9744 meters. Both answers are approximations and both are misleading. The answer 420.76 meters gives the impression that it is correct to the nearest .01 of a meter. Even more misleading, the answer 420.9744 meters gives the impression that it is correct to the nearest .0001 of a meter. How much possible error is there in the answer 420.76 meters or 420.9744 meters? The correct answer to that question is approximately three meters. In other words, the actual circumference of the circle of Figure 22 may be as small as 417 meters or as large as 423 meters. This range of accuracy makes the implied precision of answers such as 420.76 meters or 420.9744 meters, ridiculous. The central fact to be

understood here is that the use of decimal approximations for Pi
should not be construed as being equivalent to computing more
accurate answers for the circumference. The results of a computation with measurements can never be more accurate than the
original measurements.

The formula C = 2πr was used for finding the circumference of
the circle in Figure 22. The accuracy of the approximation for
Pi cannot make up for any error in the measurement of the radius. In fact, since the radius is multiplied by 2π any error in
measuring the radius is multiplied by slightly more than six in
computing the circumference. The radius 67 meters has an indicated unit of measurement of one meter. Consequently, there is
a maximum error of measurement of one-half meter ($\frac{1}{2}$ x 1). As
stated earlier, this error in measurement is multiplied by 2π
in the formula C = 2πr. Using six instead of 2π the error in
the circumference can be approximated as six times $\frac{1}{2}$ meter or
three meters.

In using the formula C = πd the possible error in computing the
circumference is approximately three times the maximum error in
measurement for the diameter. In using the formula C = 2πr the
possible error in computing the circumference is approximately
six times the maximum error in measurement for the radius.

Progress Test 7

A circle has a radius of 17 centimeters.

1.   What length is another radius for the same circle?

2.   What length is a diameter?

3.   What is the circumference of the circle?

4.   What is the approximate error that is possible in
     computing the circumference of the circle?

Exercise Set 2

I.   1.   If the error in measuring a side of each of the
          polygons below is $\frac{1}{2}$ inch, find the maximum error
          in the perimeters.

          a.   square

          b.   triangle

    c. quadrilateral

    d. hexagon

2. Which of the paths below is also a perimeter?

    a.   b.   c.   d.

3. If the side of a square is measured to the nearest foot, then the maximum error on its perimeter is ___.

4. If one side of an equilateral triangle can vary from $2\frac{3}{4}$ inches to $3\frac{1}{4}$ inches, the perimeter will vary from $8\frac{1}{4}$ inches to _____.

5. If the diameter of a piston measures 3.250 inches, the diameter may be as small as _____ or as large as _____.

6. Find perimeters for:

a. 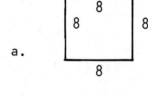   b. 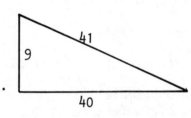   c.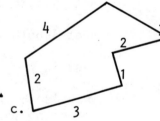

d. 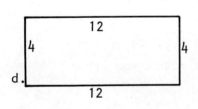   e.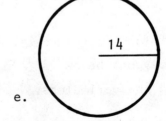

II.   Challenge Problems

1.

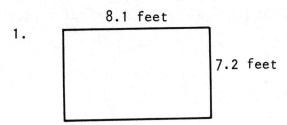

8.1 feet

7.2 feet

a.   Find the perimeter of the rectangle.

b.   Find the maximum error in the perimeter of the
     rectangle.

2.

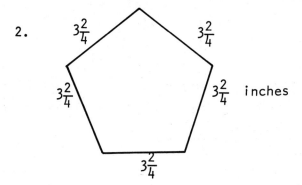

$3\frac{2}{4}$

$3\frac{2}{4}$

$3\frac{2}{4}$

$3\frac{2}{4}$ inches

$3\frac{2}{4}$

a.   Find the perimeter of the pentagon.

b.   Find the maximum error in the perimeter.

3.

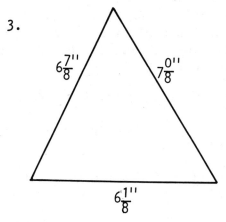

$6\frac{7''}{8}$

$7\frac{0''}{8}$

$6\frac{1''}{8}$

a.   Find the perimeter of the triangle

b.   Find the maximum error in the perimeter.

4. a. Find the circumference of the circle.

b. Find the maximum error in the circumference.

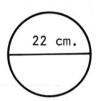

22 cm.

5. a. Find the circumference of the circle

b. Find the maximum error in the circumference.

$9\frac{4''}{16}$

6. When the measurement of a side of a regular pentagon is $7\frac{0}{8}$ inches, the perimeter can be as small as _____, or as great as _____.

AREA MEASURES

Linear measures are associated with ideas of length and distance. In this section, the topic of discussion is area measures. Area measures are associated with measuring the amount of surface enclosed by some geometric figure.

Problems such as the following involve area measures:

Ms. Aera is going to buy carpet for her living room. How much carpeting will be needed?

Mr. Erunam is planning to fertilize his lawn. How much fertilizer will be needed?

Both problems require area measures because in both cases the correct answer will depend upon the amount of surface to be covered. Ms. Aera needs to know approximately how many square yards of space are to be carpeted. Mr. Erunam needs to know approximately how many square feet of yard space needs to be fertilized.

The two figures shown below have the same perimeter.

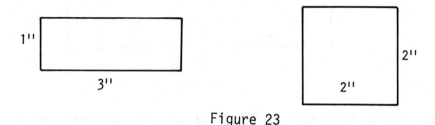

Figure 23

The rectangle and square in Figure 23 have a perimeter of 8.

$$P = 2\ell + 2w \qquad\qquad P = 4s$$

$$= 2 \cdot 3 + 2 \cdot 1 \qquad\qquad = 4 \cdot 2$$

$$= 6 + 2 \qquad\qquad\qquad = 8$$

$$= 8$$

Do the rectangle and square of Figure 23 enclose the same surface area? The answer is "No" as shown in Figure 24 below.

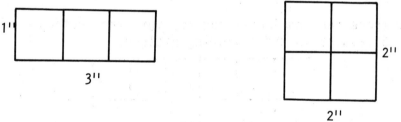

Figure 24

Inside the rectangle three one-inch squares fit snugly, but inside the square there is sufficient room for four one-inch squares. There is more surface space in the square of Figure 24 than in the rectangle.

Figure 24 shows that two geometric figures can have the same perimeter, but different areas. It also shows the basic idea behind all area measures. Area measures are always based on the idea of fitting smaller squares inside the geometric figures involved. These smaller squares are the units of measurement for the area measurement.

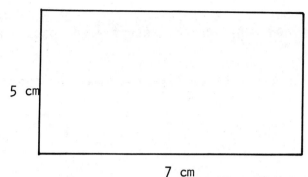

5 cm

7 cm

Figure 25

The rectangle in Figure 25 has a length of 7 cm and a width of 5 cm. To determine its area, it is necessary to (1) select a square to be used as the unit of measure, and (2) find how many such squares would be used to cover the surface area of the rectangle.

The linear unit of measure along the edges of the rectangle of Figure 25 is one centimeter. Consequently, a good sized square to use in measuring the area is a square with each side one centimeter long.

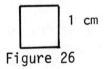

1 cm

Figure 26

Fitting these one centimeter squares into the rectangle of Figure 25 results in the following picture.

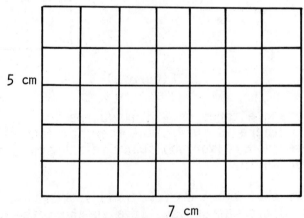

5 cm

7 cm

Figure 27

The area of the rectangle in Figure 27 is most commonly called 35 square centimeters. The term "square centimeters" in this case means one-centimeter squares. To say the area is 35 square centimeters means that the area is the same as that covered by 35 one-centimeter squares.

Progress Test 8

Find the area and perimeter of each figure below.

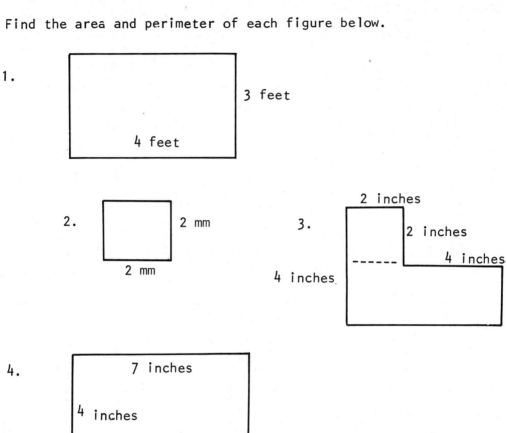

1.

3 feet

4 feet

2.   2 mm

2 mm

3.

2 inches

2 inches

4 inches

4 inches

4.

7 inches

4 inches

OTHER UNITS FOR MEASURING AREAS

Figure 28 shows a rectangle where a different unit of measure should be used for the area.

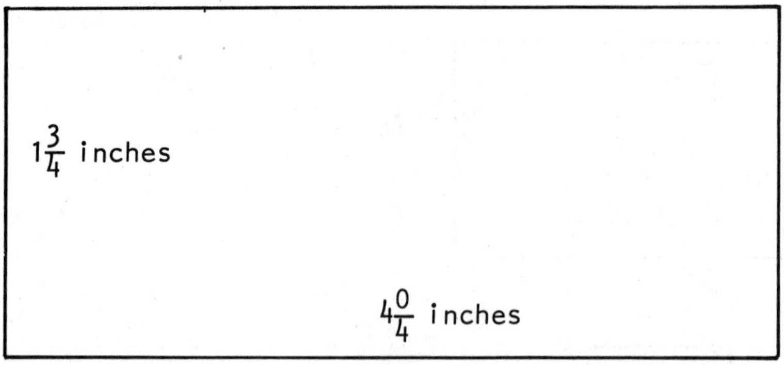

$1\frac{3}{4}$ inches

$4\frac{0}{4}$ inches

Figure 28

The linear unit of measure used for the sides of the rectangle in Figure 28 is $\frac{1}{4}$ inches. Consequently, the best choice for the area unit of measure is a square with each side $\frac{1}{4}$ inch in length.

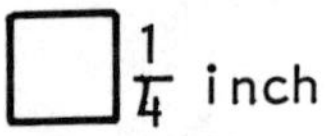

$\frac{1}{4}$ inch

Figure 29

Using $\frac{1}{4}$ inch squares the rectangle of Figure 28 could be measured as shown below.

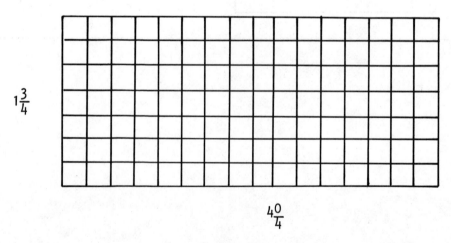

$1\frac{3}{4}$

$4\frac{0}{4}$

Figure 30

There are 112 small squares in Figure 30. The area is 112 square $\frac{1}{4}$ - inches or the same as the area covered by 112 squares each $\frac{1}{4}$ inch on a side.

The area covered by 112 squares each $\frac{1}{4}$ inch on a side is often called 7 square inches. This is because 16 $\frac{1}{4}$ - inch squares are needed to cover one 1-inch square.

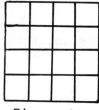

Figure 31

Seven one-inch squares would contain 7 · 16 or 112 $\frac{1}{4}$ - inch squares. Consequently, it can be claimed that 7 square inches is equal to 112 square $\frac{1}{4}$ - inches. The comparable relationship between square feet and square yards is shown in Figure 32.

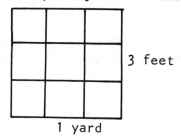

3 feet

1 yard

Figure 32

One square yard contains nine square feet. One linear yard equals three linear feet, but one square yard contains 3 · 3 or 9 square feet. Similarly, a figure showing the number of square inches in a square foot would reveal that there are 144 square inches in a square foot. One linear foot is 12 linear inches, but one square foot is 12 · 12 or 144 square inches.

How many square $\frac{1}{2}$ - inches are there in one square inch? Since there are two $\frac{1}{2}$ - inches in one inch, there are 2 · 2 or 4 square $\frac{1}{2}$ - inches in one square inch.

Although conversion figures such as 1 square yard equals 9 square feet are interesting and sometimes valuable, a word of caution is necessary at this time. Measurements are never exact; they are always approximate. In a theoretical world where measurements were exact then 1 square yard would exactly equal 9 square feet, but in the real world where all measurements are approximations, square yards and square feet imply different accuracies of measurement and different degrees of error. In the next section an example of these differences will be given.

One last important concept of area measurement needs explanation here. That concept is the Principle of Conservation. In effect, the Principle of Conservation allows the shape of a figure to be changed without changing its area. For example, the two figures below have the same area because of the Principle of Conservation.

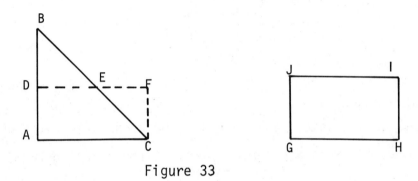

Figure 33

The isosceles triangle △ABC has the same area measure as the rectangle GHIJ. The other letters and dotted lines in Figure 33 are intended to show how the triangle can be altered to give the rectangle. If the triangle △BDE were cut off of the larger triangle △ABC and then superimposed on △EFC, the rectangle would be formed.

The Principle of Conservation will be used later to show how the formula for finding the area of any triangle is developed. Every triangle has slanting sides which would cause great troubles when trying to snugly fit little squares into them as units of measure. The Principle of Conservation makes it possible to measure every triangle in an altered shape as a rectangle.

Progress Test 9

1.   If a rectangle has sides of 2.35 meters and 4.67 meters, what is the unit of measure that should be used to find its area?

2.   What is the area of a square with each side 0.01 meter in length?

3.   What is the area of the rectangle in problem 1?

4.   Do the figures below have the same area? Why?

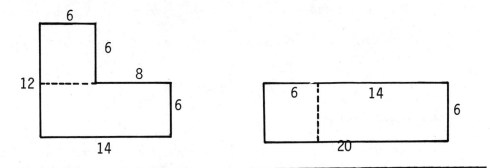

Exercise Set 3

I.   1.   Find the number of $\frac{1}{4}$ - inch squares required to cover the area of a rectangle $2\frac{1}{2}$ inches by 3 inches.

2.   A one-meter square has sides that are 100 centimeters long. How many square centimeters are needed to cover the same area as one square meter?

3.   How many square $\frac{1}{4}$ - inches are in one square inch?

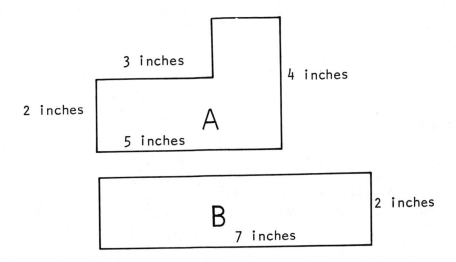

4. a. Find the area of A.
   b. Find the area of B.
   c. The chape of a figure can be changed without changing the area because of the _____ _____ _____.

5. How many square feet are needed to cover 8 square yards?

6. How many one-inch squares are needed to cover 2 square feet?

7. How many square inches equal one square yard?

II. Challenge Problems

1. The unit below is called an inch-foot. Find the area of a rectangle 9 yards by 10 yards in inch-feet.

1 inch [   ]

1 foot

2. The unit below can be called a triangle-inch. Find the area of a 3 inch square in triangle-inches.

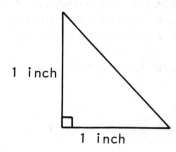

1 inch

1 inch

ERRORS IN AREA COMPUTATIONS

The formula for finding the area of a rectangle is A = ℓw where A stands for the area, ℓ for the linear measure of its length, and w for the linear measure of its width. The rationale behind the formula A = ℓw is illustrated in Figure 34.

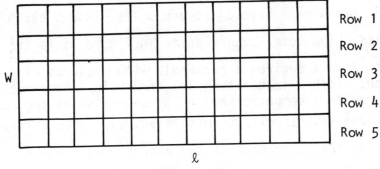

Figure 34

If a rectangle's length has linear measure ℓ then ℓ squares would
fit snugly in each row. If the rectangle's width has linear measure w then there will be w rows. Consequently, ℓ squares are
used w times and this gives the formula A = ℓw.

Using the formula A = ℓw a rectangle with length 7 inches and
width 5 inches has an area of 5 · 7 or 35 square inches. Notice that the length and width are linear measurements (inches),
but the formula gives an answer in area measurements (square
inches).

The computation of the area of a rectangle is always an approximation because the linear measures used in the computation are
approximations. Whenever two approximations are multiplied the
degree of accuracy in the answer is decreased. Consider again
the rectangle with length 7 inches and width 5 inches. The unit
of linear measure for the length and width is one inch. This
means that the maximum error of linear measurement is $\frac{1}{2}$ inch.

Suppose this maximum error did actually occur. The length could
be $6\frac{1}{2}$ inches and the width could be $4\frac{1}{2}$ inches. The drawing of
Figure 35 indicates this possibility.

1/2	1/2	1/2	1/2	1/2	1/2	1/4	Row 5
1	1	1	1	1	1	$\frac{1}{2}$	Row 4
1	1	1	1	1	1	$\frac{1}{2}$	Row 3
1	1	1	1	1	1	$\frac{1}{2}$	Row 2
1	1	1	1	1	1	$\frac{1}{2}$	Row 1

$4\frac{1}{2}$

$6\frac{1}{2}$

Figure 35

Rows 1,2,3, and 4 each have $6\frac{1}{2}$ square units. Row 5 has $3\frac{1}{4}$ square units. The total square units in Figure 35 is $29\frac{1}{4}$. This means that if we are given a rectangle with measures of length 7 inches and width 5 inches then the errors in linear measurement may lead to a computed area of 35 square units and an actual area of $29\frac{1}{4}$ square units. This relatively large difference is due to the multiplication of two approximate numbers.

Two important lessons are to be understood. First, area measures acquired by computations with linear measures have the potential for wide ranges of measuring errors. Secondly, the individual wishing a relatively accurate area computation should select a unit of linear measure with full knowledge of its implications. Area computations require the multiplication of approximations and that means the multiplication of the original measuring errors.

Progress Test 10

1.   If a rectangle has width $4\frac{1}{2}$ feet and length $8\frac{0}{2}$ feet, what is the maximum error in the measurements?

2.   What is the minimum lengths for the two sides?

3.   What is the maximum lengths for the two sides?

4.   Find the possible minimum area for the rectangle and the possible maximum area for the rectangle.

AREA FORMULAS

A square is a special type of rectangle because the length and width have the same measure. The rectangle formula $A = \ell w$ can be changed to $A = s \cdot s$ or $A = s^2$ where s stands for the length of one side of the square.

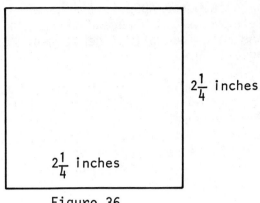

Figure 36

To compute the area of the square in Figure 36 the following steps are used:

$$A = s^2$$

$$A = (2\frac{1}{4})^2$$

$$= (\frac{9}{4})^2$$

$$= \frac{9}{4} \cdot \frac{9}{4}$$

$$= \frac{81}{16}$$

$\frac{81}{16}$ square inches is the final answer.

Every parallelogram has the same area as an associated rectangle. In Figure 37 the alteration of a parallelogram to a rectangle with the same area is shown.

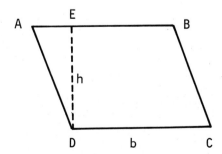 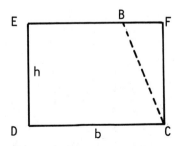

Figure 37

The area of parallelogram ABCD is the same as rectangle EFCD. On the parallelogram if ΔAED were detached and moved so that line segment $\overline{AD}$ coincided with line segment $\overline{BC}$ the result would be the rectangle EFCD.

The area of the rectangle is its length, b, times its width, h. Therefore, the area of the parallelogram is also b times h. The formula for the area of a parallelogram is A = bh, where b stands for the length of one of the sides and h stands for the perpendicular distance between the given side and its opposite. Commonly, the area of a parallelogram is called the product of its base and height (altitude).

Two parallelograms with equal perimeter measures are shown below in Figure 38.

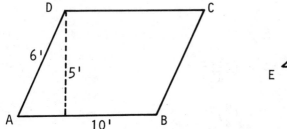
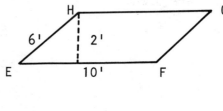

Figure 38

The perimeters of both parallelograms are 32 feet, but the areas are different. Parallelogram ABCD has area 10 · 5 or 50 square feet. Parallelogram EFGH has area 10 · 2 or 20 square feet.

Every triangle can be thought of as one-half of a parallelogram. Figure 39 illustrates that a line joining the opposite corners (vertices) of a parallelogram separates it into two congruent (same size and shape) triangles.

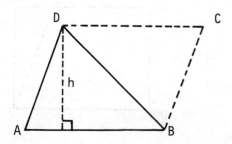
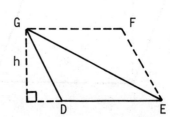

Figure 39

ΔABD is one-half of parallelogram ABCD. Since the area of parallelogram ABCD is b times h, the area of ΔABD is $\frac{1}{2}$bh. ΔDEG is
one-half of parallelogram DEFG. The formula for the area of the
parallelogram is A = bh. Consequently, the formula for the area
of the triangle is A = $\frac{1}{2}$bh, where b stands for the length of one
side and h stands for the perpendicular distance from that side
to the opposite vertex. Commonly, the area of a triangle is
said to be one-half the base times the height to that base.
A = $\frac{1}{2}$bh.

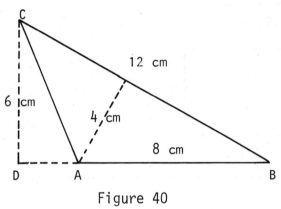

Figure 40

To find the area of triangle ABC in Figure 40 the formula A = $\frac{1}{2}$bh
can be used. The side $\overline{AB}$ can be used as the base, b, and the
segment $\overline{CD}$ would be the height, h, to that base. Notice that the
height is the perpendicular distance from point C to the line
of the base which, in this case, falls outside the triangle. Using b = 8 cm and h = 6 cm the area is $\frac{1}{2}$ · 8 · 6 or 24 square cm.

If side $\overline{BC}$ had been used as the base then its associated height
would have been 4 cm. The computation would then be as follows:

$$A = \frac{1}{2}bh$$

$$A = \frac{1}{2} \cdot 12 \cdot 4$$

$$= 24$$

The area is again 24 square cm.

Progress Test 11

Find the areas for the following figures:

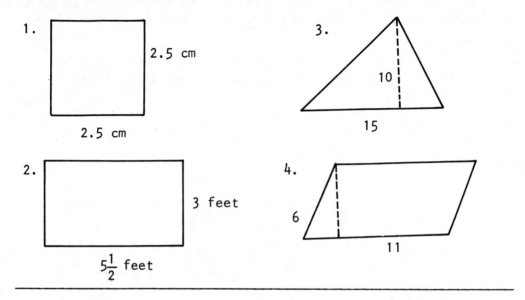

1.   2.5 cm   2.5 cm

3.   10   15

2.   3 feet $5\frac{1}{2}$ feet

4.   6   11

AREAS OF OTHER POLYGONS AND CIRCLES

The ability to compute the area of a triangle is of value in finding the area of other polygons.

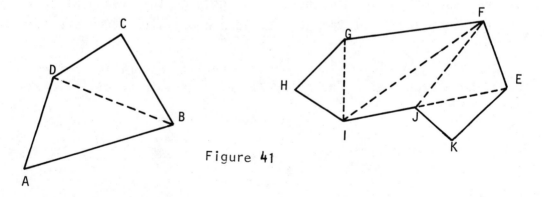

Figure 41

The areas of the polygons shown in Figure 41 can be found by separating the polygons into triangles and finding the sum of the areas of the separate triangles. Quadrilateral ABCD is not a rectangle or parallelogram and has no simple formula for its area computation. The dotted line in quadrilateral ABCD, Figure

41, shows one way of separating the quadrilateral into two triangles. The area could then be computed by the following equality:

Area Quadrilateral ABCD = Area ΔABD + Area ΔBCD. The seven-sided
polygon in Figure 41 is called a heptagon. The area of the heptagon is equal to the sum of the five triangles shown by dotted
lines in Figure 41.

In the case of a regular polygon where all sides are equal and
all angles are equal, the separation of a polygon into small triangles is most useful.

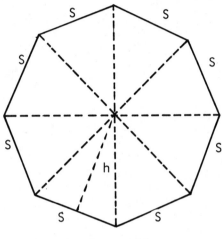

Figure 42

The figure above shows a regular octagon. The triangles drawn
into the figure use the center-point of the octagon as a common
vertex. This separation into triangles provides eight congruent
(same size and shape) triangles. The area of the octagon can be
computed by finding the area of one of the eight triangles and
multiplying the result by eight.

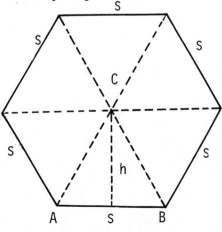

Figure 43

In Figure 43 is shown a regular hexagon with equal sides marked s and the distance from the center-point to the side marked h.

The area of the hexagon can be found by finding the area of △ABC and multiplying that result by 6, the number of congruent triangles.

$$A = (\tfrac{1}{2}sh) \cdot 6$$

This result can be generalized to any regular polygon of n sides. Again, the area of one triangle, $\tfrac{1}{2}sh$, is multiplied by the number of triangles, n. This gives the general formula for the area of a regular polygon of n sides.

$$A = (\tfrac{1}{2}sh) \cdot n$$

This formula can be written in other ways. One such interesting and useful way is

$$A = \tfrac{1}{2}h \cdot sn$$

The multiplication of s and n (sn) is the multiplication of the length of one side, s, by the number of equal sides, n. Consequently, sn is the perimeter of the regular polygon. Therefore, another form of the formula for the area of a regular polygon is

$$A = \tfrac{1}{2}h \cdot P$$

where h stands for the shortest distance from the center to the side and P stands for the perimeter of the polygon.

The formula $A = \tfrac{1}{2}h \cdot P$ is of special importance in understanding the formula for finding the area of a circle.

Figure 44

With a little imagination it is possible to consider a circle as a polygon with such a great number of short sides that they give a rounded appearance. Viewing a circle in this matter and using the formula $A = \tfrac{1}{2}h \cdot P$ provides a formula for the area of a circle.

$$A = \tfrac{1}{2}h \cdot P$$

Since a circle is under consideration, the distance between the center of the polygon and one of its sides is the radius. Therefore, r can be substituted for h to give

$$A = \frac{1}{2}r \cdot P$$

Also, since a circle is under consideration the perimeter, P, is the same as the circumference, C = 2πr. Therefore, 2πr can be substituted for P to give

$$A = \frac{1}{2}r \cdot 2\pi r$$

A little algebraic manipulation will complete the task.

$$A = \frac{1}{2}r \cdot 2\pi r$$

$$= (\frac{1}{2} \cdot 2) \; \pi \cdot r \cdot r$$

$$= 1 \cdot \pi r^2$$

$$= \pi r^2$$

The formula A = πr^2 is the result.

To find the area of a circle with radius 6 yards the following steps could be taken:

$$A = \pi r^2$$

$$= \pi \cdot 6^2$$

$$= 36\pi \; (\text{thirty-six pi})$$

The area of the circle is approximately 36π square yards. A suitable approximation for π could now be chosen to find a decimal or fractional result.

Progress Test 12

1. Find the area of the kite figure below. The two angles marked by boxes are right angles.

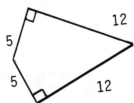

2. Find the area of a regular octagon (8 sides) with sides
    8.3 centimeters and h as the perpendicular distance from
    the center-point to the side.

3. Find the area of a circle with radius 13.3 feet. Use Pi
    as $3\frac{1}{7}$.

4. Find the area of a circle with radius 13.3 feet. Use Pi
    as 3.14.

Exercise Set 4

I.   1.   Draw $\frac{1}{2}$ inch squares in rectangle ABCD and give the area.

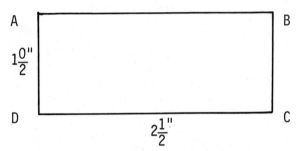

2.   Since a measurement of $1\frac{0}{2}$ inches has a maximum error of

     $\frac{1}{4}$ inch, the width and length of rectangle ABCD could be

     $1\frac{1}{4}$ inches and $2\frac{3}{4}$ inches and have a larger area.

     Draw $\frac{1}{4}$ - inch squares in rectangle HIJK and give
     the area·

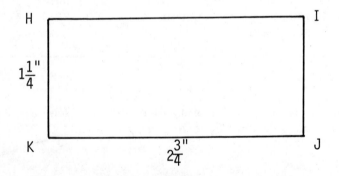

Find the area of the figures in problems 3 through 8.

3.

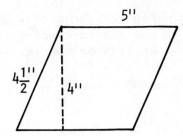

4.

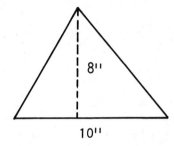

5.

6.

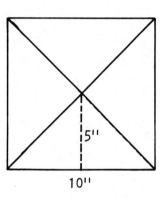

7.

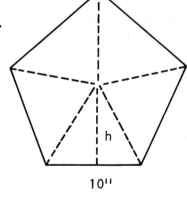

8.

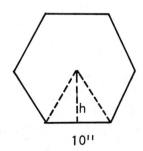

9. Find the area of a dodecagon (12 sided regular polygon) when its perimeter is 96 centimeters and h is the height of each of the 12 interior triangles.

10. Find the area of each circle below.

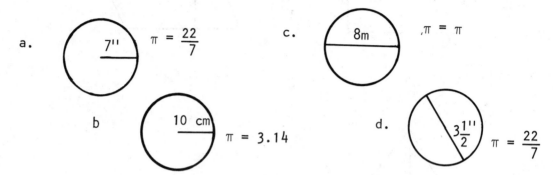

a. 7" $\pi = \dfrac{22}{7}$

c. 8m $\pi = \pi$

b   10 cm $\pi = 3.14$

d. $3\dfrac{1"}{2}$ $\pi = \dfrac{22}{7}$

II. Challenge Problems

A circle was divided into one million congruent triangles, each with its vertex at the center and an altitude almost equal to the radius, r. The triangles were rearranged as shown below to form a rectangle.

1. What is the width or height of the rectangle?

2. Why is the length of the rectangle $\dfrac{1}{2} \cdot 2\pi r$?

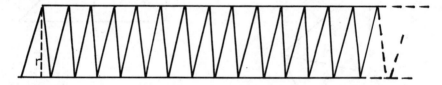

3. Since the area of the circle is the same as the area of the rectangle, use the rectangle formual A = ℓw to find the area of the circle.

VOLUME MEASURES

Linear measurements are applied in situations where the only concern is length. Theoretically a line segment has only one dimension. A line segment has length, but no width and no height. This view of line segments and linear measurements means that if we put one thousand line segments side-by-side

they would be no wider than one line segment because line segments have no width. Similarly, if one thousand line segments
were stacked one upon another the pile would be no higher than
the first line segment because line segments have no height.

Square measures are applied in situations where the object has
both length and width, but no height. Theoretically, a plane
figure like a rectangle or a circle has exactly two dimensions.
A rectangle has length and width, but no height. If we put rectangles side-by-side or end-to-end they spread out across a plane
surface taking up more space on that surface. However, if we
stack one thousand rectangles one upon another the pile would be
no higher than the first rectangle because rectangles have no
height.

Cubic measures are applied in situations where the object has
length, width, <u>and</u> height. Cubic measures are used with three
dimensional objects. Commonly, measures of three dimensional
objects are called volume measurements.

Objects such as cardboard boxes and tin cans are three-dimensional figures. Measuring the amount of space enclosed by a
cardboard box or tin can is equivalent to finding the volume
measures of the containers. The unit of measure is like that
of a child's building blocks or a pair of dice. A cube might
be called a three-dimensional square because all of its sides
(faces) are squares.

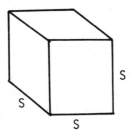

Figure 45

A cube with each side of its squares one inch long is called
one cubic inch. A cube with sides one centimeter long is called
one cubic centimeter.

The basic idea in measuring the volume of a container is filling
its space snugly with cubes.

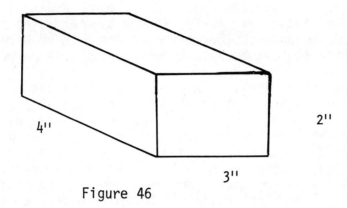

Figure 46

To measure the volume of a box like that shown in Figure 46 it is necessary to select a cube as the unit of measure and count the number of cubes required to completely fill the box. The unit of measure used for the box edges is one inch. Therefore, a good choice of a cubic unit is one cubic inch. Two views of the box are pictured below.

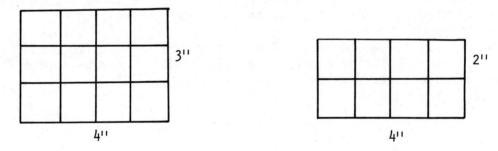

Figure 47

On the left of Figure 47 is shown a picture of the bottom of the box. It is a rectangle 4 inches long and 3 inches wide. How many cubic inches could be placed in this rectangle? The answer is 12 since one cubic inch would be required to cover each square inch of the box bottom.

On the right of Figure 47 is a side view of the box. The side view shows how many layers of blocks could be stacked in the box. Since the box is 2 inches high and each cube is one inch high there would be two layers of cubes. Each layer contains 12 cubes and with two layers there would be 2 · 12 or 24 cubes necessary to fill the box. The volume of the box in Figure 46 is 24 cubic inches.

Progress Test 13

1.   403 line segments, each 2 inches long, were stacked one
     upon the other. How high is the stack of line segments?

2.   A rectangular shaped box has a bottom 9 inches long and
     4 inches wide. What is the least number of cubes, 1 inch
     on each side, that can be used to completely cover the
     bottom of the box?

3   The box in problem 2 stands 5 inches tall. How many layers
     of cubes, 1 inch on each side, will fit in the box?

4.   What is the total number of cubes, 1 inch on each side,
     that will fit in the box?

_____

RECTANGULAR SOLIDS, CUBES, AND CYLINDERS

The basic ideas of finding volumes are (1) determining how many
cubes would cover the bottom of a container, and (2) multiplying
by the number of layers required to fill the box to the top. In
practice this procedure is equivalent to computing the area of
the base (bottom) of the container and multiplying by the height.
This computation for finding the volume of a container is shown
in the following formula:

$$V = Ah$$

In the formula $V = Ah$, V stands for the volume, A stands for the
area of the base, and h stands for the height.

For the rectangular box in Figure 46, the formula $V = Ah$ may be
written as $V = \ell wh$ because $A = \ell w$. Since $\ell = 4$ inches, w = 3
inches and h = 2 inches, the computation of the box's volume is
completed as shown below:

$$V = \ell wh$$

$$= 4 \cdot 3 \cdot 2$$

$$= 24$$

24 cubic inches is the volume, using the formula.

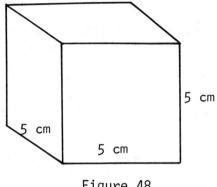

Figure 48

In Figure 48 is shown a cube 5 cm on a side.   Its volume can be
determined by the formula $V = Ah$ or by the formula $V = s^3$.
$V = Ah$ is equivalent to $V = s^3$ for finding the volume of a cube
because $A = s^2$ and $h = s$.

To find the volume of the cube in Figure 48 the following steps
are used:

$$V = Ah$$

$$= s^3$$

$$= 5^3$$

$$= 5 \cdot 5 \cdot 5$$

$$= 125$$

125 cubic cm is the volume of the cube in Figure 48.

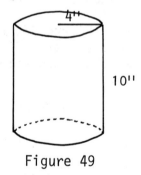

Figure 49

Figure 49 shows a cylinder.   It has a circle with radius 4 inches
as its base.   The height of the cylinder is 10 inches.   To find
the volume of the cylinder the formula $V = Ah$ or the formula

$V = \pi r^2 h$ may be used.   V = Ah is equivalent to $V = \pi r^2 h$ because the area of the circular base, A, is equal to πr^2.

The computation of the volume of the cylinder is shown below:

$$V = Ah$$

$$V = \pi r^2 h$$

$$= \pi \cdot 4^2 \cdot 10$$

$$= \pi \cdot 16 \cdot 10$$

$$= \pi \cdot 160$$

$$= 160\pi$$

160π cubic inches is the volume of the cylinder in Figure 49.

Volume computations are always the product (multiplication) of three linear measurements. Since linear measurements are always approximations and since these approximations are multiplied, volume answers have the potential for much greater errors than the original measures might suggest. Where a particular degree of accuracy is required in a volume computation the unit of linear measure must be chosen carefully to insure that accuracy.

Progress Test 14

1.   Find the volume of a rectangular solid 6 centimeters long, 2 centimeters wide, and 5 centimeters high.

2.   Find the volume of a cube with sides 4.2 feet in length.

3.   Find the volume of a cylinder with radius 10 inches and height 21 inches. Use $3\frac{1}{7}$ for Pi.

4.   How many cubic feet are in a cubic yard?

Exercise Set 5

I.   1.   Find the volume of the box shown below.

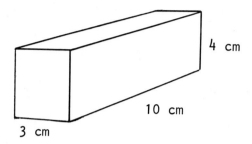

4 cm

10 cm

3 cm

2.   Find the volume of the cylinder.   Use $\frac{22}{7}$ for pi.

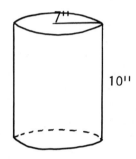

7"

10"

3.   Find the volume of a cube 6.3 centimeters on a side.

4.   Find the volume of a rectangular shaped swimming pool 30' by 20' by 8'.

5.   Find the volume of a cylindrical oil tank, 100 feet in diameter and 30 feet high.

6.   How many cubic inches are in a cubic foot?

7.   How many cubic centimeters are in a cubic meter?

II.   Challenge Problems

1.   A rectangular shaped box has measurements of 8 centimeters by 3 centimeters by 5 centimeters.

a.   What is the maximum error in measurement for each side?

b.   Find the volume of the box.

c.   Find the volume of the box if all three measures have a maximum error and are actually shorter.

d.   Find the volume of the box if all three measures have a maximum error and are actually longer.

2.   Find the weight of the water filling a cylindrical tank 10 feet high and 14 feet in diameter using $\frac{22}{7}$ as an approximation for pi and 62.4 lbs. as the weight of one cubic foot of water.

3.   If a diver has 10 square feet of body area and is swimming 30 feet down, find the weight of water pressing on his body using 62.4 pounds as the weight of one cubic foot of water.

4.   The volume of a solid is the area of the base times the height.

$$V = Ah$$

Find the volume of the column below that has a triangular base.

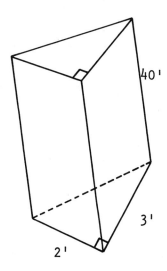

MODULE SELF-TEST

1. Which of the following sentences contain approximate numbers.

    a. There are 16 students in Mary's class.

    b. A track is 440 yards long.

    c. Juliana weighs 110 3/4 pounds.

    d. The sign was 4 feet, $8\frac{9}{10}$ inches tall

    e. Mose ran seventh at the turn.

2. Is it possible to measure a line segment correctly with two different rulers and arrive at different answers?

3. What is the unit of measure for each of the rulers shown?

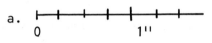

4. What is the maximum error of measurement when the unit of measure is:

    a. $\frac{1}{2}$ millimeter

    b. 1 meter

    c. $\frac{1}{4}$ inch

5. Find the largest unit of measure that could be used if the following errors could be tolerated:

    a. $\frac{1}{4}$ inch

    b. 8 inches

    c. 0.4 centimeter

6. What unit of measure is indicated by each of the following
    measurements:

    a. $7\frac{3}{8}$ inches

    b. $3\frac{0}{8}$ inches

    c. 7.0 centimeters

7. 100 meters is an ambiguous measure because its _____
    __ _____ is not clearly indicated.

8. What does the Principle of Conservation mean in terms
    of the length of a piece of rope?

9. Which one of the following is a perimeter path?

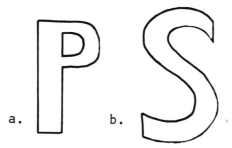

    a.   b.

10. Using the measurements shown, what is the maximum error
     involved in finding the perimeter of the figure?

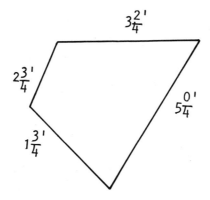

11.   Find perimeters for:

    a. A square with side 9.2 meters.

    b. A regular hexagon with side $5\frac{3}{4}$ inches.

    c. A parallelogram with sides of 9 meters and 5 meters.

12.   Find areas for:

    a. A triangle with base $2\frac{5}{8}$ inches and height $4\frac{0}{8}$ inches.

    b. A rectangle with length 4.8 cm and width 3.7 cm.

    c. A circle with radius 100 yards.

PROGRESS TEST ANSWERS

Progress Test 1

1.   b

2.   true

3.   false

4.   true

Progress Test 2

1. $\frac{1}{8}$ inch

2.   1 inch

3.   They have different units of measure and different degrees of accuracy.

4.   30 yards, 0 inches

Progress Test 3

1.   18 inches

2.   36 cm

3.   No. A rubber band is elastic

Progress Test 4

1.   A

2.   20, 30

3.   regular

Progress Test 5

1.   parallelogram, 12

2.   trapezoid, 40

3.   square, 44

4.   rectangle, 28

Progress Test 6

1.   32.9 m

2.   0.05 m

3.   0.35 m

4.   32.55 m, 33.25 m

Progress Test 7

1. 17 cm

2. 34 cm

3. 34π cm or 107 cm

4. 3 cm

Progress Test 8

1. P = 14 feet, A = 12 sq. ft.

2. P = 8 mm, A = 4 sq. mm

3. P = 20 in, A = 16 sq. in.

4. P = 22 in., A = 28 sq. in.

Progress Test 9

1. squares with sides 0.01m in length

2. 0.0001 sq. m

3. 10.97 sq. m

4. Yes, Principle of Conservation

Progress Test 10

1. $\frac{1}{4}$ foot

2. $4\frac{1}{4}$ feet, $7\frac{3}{4}$ feet

3. $4\frac{3}{4}$ feet, $8\frac{1}{4}$ feet

4. $\frac{527}{16}$ sq. ft., $\frac{627}{16}$ sq. ft.

Progress Test 11

1. 6.25 sq. cm

2. $16\frac{1}{2}$ sq. ft.

Progress Test 11 (continued)

3. 75 sq. units

4. 55 sq. units

Progress Test 12

1. 60 sq. units

2. 33.2h cm

3. 555.94 sq. cm

4. 545.4346 sq. cm

Progress Test 13

1. No height

2. 36

3. 5

4. 180

Progress Test 14

1. 60 cubic cm

2. 74 cubic cm

3. 6600 cubic in.

4. 27

EXERCISE SET ANSWERS

Exercise Set 1

I.   1.   a. $\frac{1}{4}$ inch   b. $\frac{1}{2}$ inch   c. $\frac{1}{8}$ inch   d. 0.1 cm

2.   a. $1\frac{1}{4}$ inch $1\frac{1}{2}$ inch $1\frac{3}{8}$ inch   3 cm

b. $2\frac{1}{4}$ inch $2\frac{0}{2}$ inch $2\frac{1}{8}$ inch   6 cm

3.   a. $\frac{1}{2}$ inch   b. $\frac{1}{8}$ inch   c. 0.5 cm

d. $\frac{1}{64}$ inch   e. $\frac{1}{16}$ inch   f. 0.05 inch

4.   a. $\frac{1}{2}$ inch   b. 0.1 inch   c. $\frac{1}{16}$ inch

d. $\frac{1}{64}$ inch   e. 1 m   f. 0.01 cm

5.   18 feet, $5\frac{1}{2}$ inches,   18 feet, $6\frac{1}{2}$ inches

6.   Principle of Conservation

II.   1.   a, c

2.   a. $1\frac{3}{16}$ inches   b. Different units of measure

3.   0.1 cm because 0.1 cm is smaller than 0.1 inches.

4. $4\frac{0}{2}$ inches

5.   0.002 inch

Exercise Set 2

I.   1.   a. 2 inches   b. $1\frac{1}{2}$ inches   c. 2 inches   d. 3 inches

2.   a, b

3.   2 feet

Exercise Set 2 (continued)

4. $9\frac{3}{4}$ inches

5. 3.2495 inches,   3.2505 inches

6. a. 32 b. 90 c. 15 d. 32 e. 88

II. 1. a. 30.6 feet   b. 0.2 feet

2. a. $17\frac{1}{2}$ inches   b. $\frac{5}{8}$ inch

3. a. 20 inches   b. $\frac{3}{16}$ inch

4. a. 22π cm   b. 1.5 cm

5. a. $\frac{37}{2}\pi$ inches   b. $\frac{3}{16}$ inch

6. $34\frac{11}{16}$ inches, $35\frac{5}{16}$ inches

Exercise Set 3

I. 1. 120

2. 10,000

3. 16

4. a. 14 sq. in. b. 14 sq. in.   c. Principle of Conservation

5. 72 sq. ft.

6. 288

7. 1296

II. 1. 9720 inch-feet

2. 18 triangle-inches

Exercise Set 4

I.   1.   10 square half-inches

2.   55 sq. $\frac{1}{4}$ inches

3.   20 sq. in.

4.   20 sq. in.

5.   40 sq. in.

6.   100 sq. in.

7.   25h sq. in.

8.   30h sq. in.

9.   48h sq. cm

10.   a.   154 sq. in.   b.   314 sq. cm.   c.   16π sq. m

d. $\frac{77}{8}$ sq. in.

II.   1.   r

2.   The bases of half the triangles form the length. Since the sum of all the triangle bases is the circumference, 2πr, the length will be $\frac{1}{2}$ · 2πr.

3.   A = ℓw

$$= r \cdot \frac{1}{2} \cdot 2\pi r$$

$$= \pi r^2$$

Exercise Set 5

I.   1.   120 cubic cm

2.   1540 cubic in.

3.   250 cubic cm

4.   4800 cubic ft.

5.   235,500 cubic ft.

Exercise Set 5 (continued)

6. 1728

7. 1,000,000 cubic cm

II. 1. a. 0.5 cm   b.   120 cubic cm   c.   84 cubic cm

d.   163 cubic cm

2. 96,096 lbs.

3. 18,720 lbs.

4. 120 cubic feet

MODULE SELF-TEST ANSWERS

1. b, c, d

2. Yes

3. a. $\frac{1}{4}$ inch   b. $\frac{1}{2}$ inch   c. $\frac{1}{8}$ inch

4. a. $\frac{1}{4}$ mm   b. $\frac{1}{2}$ m   c. $\frac{1}{8}$ inch

5. a. $\frac{1}{2}$ inch   b. 16 inches   c. 0.8 cm

6. a. $\frac{1}{8}$ inch   b. $\frac{1}{8}$ inch   c. 0.1 cm

7. unit of measure

8. Its length does not change when its shape is altered.

9. b

10. $\frac{4}{8}$ inch

11. a. 36.8 m   b. $34\frac{1}{2}$ inches   c. 28 m

12. a. $5\frac{1}{4}$ sq. in. b. 17.76 sq. cm   c.   31,400 sq. yards

13. a. 1331 cubic cm b. 36 cubic ft.   c.   3,080 cubic in.

REVIEW EXERCISE SETS

1. Give the unit of measure when the maximum error in a
    measurement is:

    a. $\frac{1}{2}$ inch   b. $\frac{1}{4}$ inch   c. $\frac{1}{16}$ inch

    d. 1 foot   e. 0.05 cm

2. Give the maximum error that would exist using the following
    units of measure:

    a. 1 foot   b. 1 mile   c. 0.1 cm

    d. $\frac{1}{16}$ inch   e. 0.1 mm   f. 0.004 cm

3. Find the maximum error using a ruler with:

    a. 3 markings between each inch.

    b. 15 markings between each inch.

    c. 9 markings between each centimeter.

    d. 1 marking between each foot.

4. Find the maximum and minimum possible lengths of rods
    said to be :

    a. 8 feet $3\frac{1}{2}$ inches long measured with a ruler marked off
        in $\frac{1}{2}$ inches.

    b. 13.8 centimeters long measured with a meter stick
        marked off in one-tenths of a centimeter.

    c. $9\frac{7}{8}$ inches long measured with a ruler marked off in $\frac{1}{16}$
        inches.

5. The length of a rope does not change regardless of its
    position because of the _____ __ _____.

6. Which of the following are approximations?

    a. There are 100 United States Senators.

    b. Homer is driving 55 miles per hour.

c. Joe got 15 questions out of 20 correct on a test.

d. Ted's blood pressure was measured as 120 over 80.

7. What unit of measure should be used by a watch maker that must work with an acceptable margin of error of 0.02 cm?

Review Exercise Set 2

1. If the maximum error in measuring a side of each of the polygons below is $\frac{1}{4}$ inch, find the maximum error in the perimeters.

    a. square   b. triangle   c. quadrilateral   d. hexagon

2. Name the capital letters of the alphabet that are perimeter paths.

3. Give the maximum error in the perimeter of a square if its side is measured to the nearest:

    a. $\frac{1}{4}$ inch,   b. centimeter   c. 0.1 mm

4. If one side of an equilateral pentagon can vary from $3\frac{1}{8}$ inches to $2\frac{7}{8}$ inches the perimeter will vary from _____ to _____.

5. If the diameter of an exhaust valve in an engine measures 2.120 inches the diameter may be as small as _____ or as large as _____ .

6. Find perimeters for:

a.

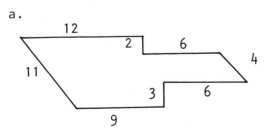

b.

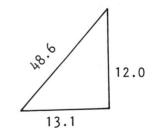

c.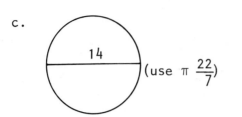

(use π $\frac{22}{7}$)

d.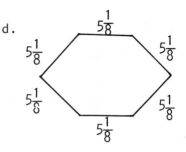

7.   Find the maximum error in the perimeter of figure 6 b.

8.   If a circle has a radius of 9 millimeters:

   a.   what is the length of its diameter?

   b.   how long is another radius?

   c.   what is the circumference of the circle: (Use Pi = 3.14.)

   d.   The circumference can be as short as _____ or as
         long as _____ .

Review Exercise Set 3

1.   A one-meter square has sides that are 1,000 millimeters
      long. How many square millimeters are needed to cover
      the same area as one square meter?

2.   Find the number of $\frac{1}{8}$ inch squares required to cover the
      area of a rectangle $3\frac{3}{4}$ inches by $5\frac{1}{2}$ inches.

3.   How many square feet are in one square yard?

4.   Find the area and perimeter of each of the following
      figures:

a.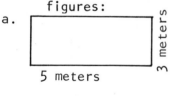
5 meters

b.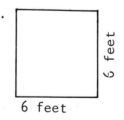
6 feet

c.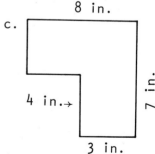

d.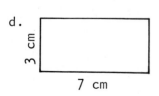
7 cm

5. How many $\frac{1}{2}$ foot squares would fit in figure 4 b?

6. There are 100 centimeters in one meter. How many square centimeters are needed to cover one square meter?

7. If 48 one-quarter inch squares are contained in a figure, how many one-eighth inch squares will it contain?

8. A rectangular plot of land 30 feet wide and 1,452 feet long has an area of exactly one acre. A square mile has sides 5,280 feet long. How many acres are there in a square mile?

9. How many square feet are there in a rug 12 square yards in area?

Review Exercise Set 4

1. If a square is $4\frac{2}{4}$ centimeters long on each side:

    a. Find the minimum length of a side.

    b. Find the maximum length of a side.

    c. Find the maximum area and the minimum area.

2. If a rectangle measures $5\frac{1}{2}$ feet wide and $7\frac{0}{2}$ feet long:

    a. Find the minimum length of the two sides.

    b. Find the maximum length of the two sides.

    c. Find the maximum area and the minimum area.

3. Find the area of:

    a. a triangle with a base 4.5 meters long and a height 3.0 meters high

    b. a rectangle $3\frac{1}{4}$ inches wide and $5\frac{2}{4}$ inches long

    c. a parallelogram with a base 12.4 mm long and a height 5.7 mm high.

4. Find the area of a regular pentagon with sides 2.34 cm long and h as the length of the perpendicular distance from the center to a side.

5. Find the area of a circle with a radius 21 yards long. Use Pi as $3\frac{1}{7}$.

6. Find the area of a circle with a diameter 8.6 meters long. Use Pi as 3.14. Round the answer to the nearest one-tenth.

7. Find the area of a regular octagon with sides 9 inches long and h as the length of the perpendicular distance from the center to a side.

Review Exercise Set 5

1. Find the volume of a rectangular box 6 cm wide, 8 cm high and 12 cm long.

2. Find the volume of a cylinder 12 feet high with a diameter of 14 feet. Use $\frac{22}{7}$ as Pi.

3. How many cubic inches are there in a cubic yard?

4. Find the volume, to the nearest one-tenth, of a cube with sides 5.1 mm long.

5. If a cubic centimeter of a material weighs 20 grams, what would a cubic meter of the substance weigh? 100 centimeters = 1 meter.

6. If a cubic centimeter of a metal weighs 80 grams, what would a cubic millimeter of the metal weigh? 10 millimeters = 1 centimeter.

7. If a boxcar is 12 feet wide, 60 feet long and 10 feet high:

   a. How many boxes one foot on each side would be needed to cover the floor one box thick?

   b. If each box weighs 8.7 pounds, what is the weight of the maximum number of boxes that can be put in the boxcar?

REVIEW EXERCISE SET ANSWERS

Review Exercise Set 1

1. a. 1 inch   b. $\frac{1}{2}$ inch   c. $\frac{1}{8}$ inch   d. 2 feet   e. 0.1 cm

2. a. $\frac{1}{2}$ foot   b. $\frac{1}{2}$ mile   c. 0.05 cm   d. $\frac{1}{32}$ inch

    e. 0.05 mm   f. 0.002 cm

3. a. $\frac{1}{8}$ inch   b. $\frac{1}{32}$ inch   c. 0.05 cm   d. $\frac{1}{4}$ foot

4. a. 8 feet $3\frac{3}{4}$ in., 8 feet $3\frac{1}{4}$ in.   b. 13.85 cm, 13.75 cm

    c. $\frac{29}{32}$ in., $9\frac{27}{32}$ in.

5. Principle of Conservation   6. b, d   7. 0.04 cm

Review Exercise Set 2

1. a. 1 in.   b. $\frac{3}{4}$ in.   c. 1 in.   d. $\frac{6}{4}$ in.

2. D, 0

3. a. $\frac{1}{2}$ in.   b. 2 cm   c. 0.2 mm

4. $15\frac{5}{8}$ in. to $14\frac{3}{8}$ in.   5. 2.1195 in., 2.1205 in.

6. a. 53   b. 73.7   c. 44   d. $30\frac{3}{4}$

7. 0.15

8. a. 18 mm   b. 9 mm   c. 56.52 mm   d. 55.02, 58.02

Review Exercise Set 3

1. 1,000,000   2. 968   3. 9

4. a. 15 sq. m, 16 m   b. 36 sq. ft., 24 ft.

    c. 36 sq. in., 30 in.   d. 21 sq. cm, 20 cm

5. 144   6. 10,000   7. 192   8. 640   9. 108

Review Exercise Set 4

1. a. $43\frac{3}{8}$ cm   b. $45\frac{5}{8}$ cm   c. $21\frac{25}{64}$ sq. cm, $19\frac{9}{64}$ sq. cm

2. a. $5\frac{1}{4}$ ft., $6\frac{3}{4}$ ft.   b. $5\frac{3}{4}$ ft., $7\frac{1}{4}$ ft.

    c. $41\frac{11}{16}$ sq. ft., $35\frac{7}{16}$ sq. ft.

3. a. 6.75 sq. m   b. $17\frac{7}{8}$ sq. in.   c. 70.68 sq. mm

4. 5.85h sq. cm   5. 1386 sq. yds.

6. 58.1 sq. m   7. 36h sq. in.

Review Exercise Set 5

1. 576 cu. cm   2. 1848 cu. ft.   3. 46,656

4. 132.7 cu. mm   5. 20,000,000 grams   6. 0.08 grams

7. a. 720   b. 62,640 pounds